THE Big MistaKe

and Other StoriEs

Editor: Rosalba Foreman
Design: Nadia Maestri
Illustrations: Mario Benvenuto, Enzo Marciante, Nicola Rovetta

Stories by Bruna Deriu.
Activities and footnotes by Nella Burnett-Stuart.

© 1996 Cideb Editrice, Genoa
© Full colour edition: 1998

First edition: May 1996

We would be happy to receive your comments and suggestions,
and give you any other information concerning our material.
editorial@blackcat-cideb.com
www.blackcat-cideb.com
www.cideb.it

CISQ CISQ CERT
TEXTBOOKS AND
TEACHING MATERIALS
The quality of the publisher's
design, production and sales processes has
been certified to the standard of
UNI EN ISO 9001

ISBN 978-88-7754-775-0 Book + CD

Printed in Italy by Litoprint, Genoa

Contents

 These symbols indicate the beginning and the end of the passages linked to the listening activities.

PHONETIC SYMBOLS

Vowels

[ɪ]	*as in*	six
[i]	"	happy
[iː]	"	see
[e]	"	red
[æ]	"	hat
[ɑː]	"	car
[ɒ]	"	dog
[ɔː]	"	door
[ʊ]	"	put
[uː]	"	food
[ʌ]	"	cup
[ə]	"	about
[ɜː]	"	girl

Diphthongs

[eɪ]	*as in*	made
[aɪ]	"	five
[aʊ]	"	house
[ɔɪ]	"	boy
[əʊ]	"	home
[ɪə]	"	beer
[eə]	"	hair
[ʊə]	"	poor

Consonants

[b]	*as in*	bed
[k]	"	cat
[tʃ]	"	church
[d]	"	day
[f]	"	foot
[g]	"	good
[dʒ]	"	page
[h]	"	how
[j]	"	yes
[l]	"	leg
[m]	"	mum
[n]	"	nine
[ŋ]	"	sing
[p]	"	pen
[r]	"	red
[s]	"	soon
[z]	"	zoo
[ʃ]	"	show
[ʒ]	"	measure
[t]	"	tea
[θ]	"	thin
[ð]	"	this
[v]	"	voice
[w]	"	wine

[']   represents primary stress in the syllable which follows

[,]   represents secondary stress in the syllable which follows

[r]   indicates that the final "r" is only pronounced before a word beginning with a vowel sound (British English). In American English, the "r" is usually pronounced before both consonants and vowel sounds.

Before reading

1 Look at the words in the box and decide which job is:

- the most exciting ....
- the most interesting ....
- the most difficult ....
- the most well-paid ....
- the most dangerous ....

> teacher   plumber   policeman   detective   lawyer
> builder   lorry driver   miner   politician
> accountant   nurse   librarian   butler   artist

Which job would you like to do? Why?

....

Which job wouldn't you like to do? Why?

....

2 Look at the list below:

Parts of the body ....

Food ....

Weather ....

Furniture ....

Buildings ....

Now read the story and find words that go into each category.

A CaSE

of Trust

The tall man in uniform knocked nervously on the
office door. Detective Miller wanted to see him
but he had no idea why. The door opened. Miller
smiled and beckoned [1] with his hand.

'Come in,' he said, closing the door behind them.   5

'John Baker, sir.' The younger man said.

'Yes. I know who you are. Relax, don't be so nervous!'
Miller replied. 'Sit down'.

'Thank you, sir.'

Baker was worried. It was the first time that Miller had   10
called him to his office. He sat down, hoping there was
nothing wrong. Miller sat opposite him. There was silence for

---

1. **beckoned** : signalled.

a few seconds. After a while, Miller cleared his throat and
spoke.

15   'Listen, Baker. The head office has asked me for a list of my
best men. They want to promote somebody in this office.'

Baker sat forward on his chair.

'Promotion, sir?' he asked.

'Yes, Baker. I'm thinking of giving them your name.

20   'Thank you, sir,' Baker replied excitedly.

'Don't thank me yet. I've heard good things about you. Your
colleagues call you "the brain" – I presume it's because of
your intelligence...' Miller said, opening the drawer in his
desk. Baker shrugged [1] his shoulders modestly. Miller took a

25 folder [2] out of the drawer and handed it to him.

'Read this,' he said, staring at the desk in front of him as he
spoke. 'It's a strange case – see what you can make of it. [3] Take
it with you. When you've solved it, bring it back. Don't forget
that your promotion could depend on the solution!'

30   Miller stood up and Baker realized that it was time for him
to go. He thanked Miller and left the office cheerfully. He
looked quickly at the clock and saw that it was almost
midday. Time for his lunch-break. Good. He could read the
case, and hopefully solve it by the end of the day. The

35 promotion would soon be his.

---

1. **shrugged** : lifted (his shoulders).
2. **folder** : folded piece of card used for holding papers.
3. **see what you can make of it** : see if you can understand it.

As usual, his desk was untidy. He pushed the papers to one side to make room [1] for his sandwiches. He connected the telephone answering machine, so as not to be disturbed. Then, he opened the folder, and began to read the contents.

40   William Cranberry woke up with a strange idea in mind. He wanted to go to the public library but couldn't understand why. He'd never been there before and his own personal library was full of books that he had never read. He told his butler,[2] Jenkins, of his plans and after breakfast, Jenkins took
45 the car out of the garage. They drove to the library and William Cranberry went in alone. As he walked around the bookshelves, he was approached by a librarian. She asked if he was looking for anything in particular. Without thinking, William Cranberry asked for *Strange Destiny*, by a certain
50 B. Dale. He didn't know why he had asked for that particular book as he had never heard of it before. The librarian moved away and then came back with a small book. William Cranberry took it and thanked her. When he opened the book, a piece of paper fell to the floor.
55   He picked it up and read it. It was a receipt [3] from the local pawnshop.[4] Somebody had left it in the book. William

---

1.   **make room** : make space.
2.   **butler** : chief male servant of the house.
3.   **receipt** [rɪ'siːt] : written piece of paper which states something has been paid.
4.   **pawnshop** ['pɔːnʃɒp] : see note 1 on page 12.

Cranberry was a curious man – he wanted to know what had been pawned. He left the library immediately and went to see the pawnbroker. [1] He gave in the receipt and bought back the
60 pawned item. It was a small antique, silver mirror that was probably worth [2] a lot of money. William Cranberry was pleased with his purchase. He took it home and cleaned it carefully. As he was cleaning it, he noticed that the handle was loose. [3] He unscrewed [4] the handle and found a visiting
65 card inside. He read the card:

> **Madame Eve, Clairvoyant. [5]**
> **10 Rosehip Lane**
> **London SW6**

William Cranberry had a problem. His business was not going well – he had lost a lot of money due to a careless [6] investment. He had never been to see a clairvoyant before so perhaps she could give him some good advice. Besides, the
70 series of coincidences that had made him find the visiting

---

1. **pawnbroker** : person to whom people bring expensive items (a pawn) so that he will lend them money. If the money is not repaid within a certain time he can sell the items. A pawnbroker works in a pawnshop.
2. **worth** : has the value of.
3. **loose** : not firmly fixed.
4. **unscrewed** [ʌnˈskruːd] : removed the screws (a 'screw' is similar to a nail).
5. **Clairvoyant** : person who is able to see in the future.
6. **careless** : not careful.

A CasE of Trust

card meant that fate [1] wanted him to go there. Without telling anyone, he made an appointment with Madame Eve.

He found the house easily. Madame Eve opened the door. Cranberry was expecting to see a strange woman wearing eccentric clothes and carrying a crystal ball. Madame Eve, however, looked very ordinary – middle-aged and very serious. She showed him into an empty room. There were only two small wooden chairs for them to sit on. She explained that she was changing the furniture, and that she was waiting for the delivery [2] that evening.

Cranberry was sure that he had never seen her before in his life, yet she knew everything about him. Even private things. She knew about his old girlfriends, she described his home and gave details of his childhood. William Cranberry was amazed because he had never believed in such things. He wanted to know more and at the end of his visit, she gave him the advice he asked for. She told him that his bad luck was caused by a jealous spirit. To free himself of this bad luck, he had to take his most expensive heirloom [3] and bury [4] it in his mother's grave [5] for three days. Within three days his luck would change for the better.

1. **fate** : destiny.
2. **for the delivery** : for the furniture to be brought to the house.
3. **heirloom** : valuable possessions belonging to his ancestors.
4. **bury** : put it under ground.
5. **grave** : place in the ground where a dead person is buried.

This is what William Cranberry did. He took the diamond necklace that had belonged to his great-grandmother, out of the safe. [1] It was very old, and was worth thousands of pounds. He wrapped it carefully in a black

100 cloth, and put it into a plastic bag. Wearing old and torn [2] clothes, he went to the cemetery [3] after dark. He made sure that there was nobody around and then buried the necklace.

Unfortunately for William, things went from worse to worse over the next few days. He lost more money on the stock
105 exchange and caught the flu. [4] Then his butler, Jenkins went away for a few days; his mother was very ill, and he wanted to see her before she died. William Cranberry's luck had not changed at all. On the fourth day, he returned to the cemetery. Once again, he dug up his mother's grave. He couldn't find the
110 necklace. He dug even deeper, but it was useless. Someone had stolen it! Annoyed with himself for his stupidity, he went to see Madame Eve. To his surprise and anger, Madame Eve had disappeared. The house was empty, and he had no way of

---

1. **safe** : usually a metal box in which money and valuables are kept.
2. **torn** : his clothes were in pieces.
3. **cemetery** : piece of land used for burying dead people.
4. **flu** : influenza.

finding her. He suspected that she was responsible but he
didn't know how to prove it. He didn't want to ruin his   115
reputation so he decided not to report it to the police. He tried
to forget the incident.

Who stole the necklace? How did Madame Eve know about
his past history? Why did William Cranberry want to go to the
library?   120

Baker finished his lunch, and closed the folder. He had
read the story carefully, and had already solved the mystery.
He would soon be promoted, and all for a few minutes' work!
He put a piece of paper into his typewriter, and began to type
out his answer.   125

Madame Eve had learned about William's life from her
accomplice, the butler. They had planned the theft together.
The butler had hidden a small microphone in William
Cranberry's pillow. [1] At night, a cassette-recording would
repeat the orders, 'Go to the library, ask for *Strange Destiny*.'   130
In the morning Cranberry remembered the orders without
knowing why. The butler knew that Cranberry was a curious
man and would not be able to resist a pawnbroker's receipt.
He also knew that he had lost a lot of money, and would do
anything to improve his business affairs. The clairvoyant   135
convinced him that she could see the future, because she
knew everything about his past. Her house was already empty
and, together with the butler, they had already planned their

1. **pillow** :

escape. He did not suspect her at all, and took her advice
140 without hesitation.

Baker put his written answer on top of the folder and
headed back [1] to Miller's office. He knocked and entered.

'Already?' Miller exclaimed.

'Yes, Sir.' Baker replied proudly.

145 Miller opened the folder and re-read the story. Then he
read Baker's reply. During this time Baker sat silently.
Suddenly Miller began to laugh, and he shook his head
disbelievingly. [2]

'Who'd have thought!' he cried. 'Well done, Baker. You've
150 certainly lived up to [3] your reputation!'

'Thank you, sir.'

Miller put the folder back into the drawer of his desk. He
stood and accompanied Baker to the door.

'Don't come to work tomorrow. Take a week's holiday. When
155 you return next Monday, you'll hear about the promotion.'

'Thank you, sir,' Baker replied.

He left the office and thought of the promotion for the rest of
the day. When he got home, he told his wife about it. She was
pleased, and insisted on celebrating the event. They took some
160 of their savings [4] out of the bank, and went abroad for five days.

---

1. **headed back** : returned.
2. **disbelievingly** : not believing.
3. **lived up to** : reached the standard that was expected.
4. **savings** : money which is put away over a period of time.

A CasE of Trust

Monday morning soon arrived, and Baker returned to work. He wanted to see Miller. He went to the office and knocked on the door. He opened it and went in, but Miller wasn't there. A man was sitting at his desk.

'Yes?' The man looked up. 165

'Umm, I was looking for Detective Miller, sir,' Baker replied.

'I've taken his place. [1] You must be John Baker. Is there something I can do for you?'

'No, that's alright, thank you,' Baker replied.

He left the office and went to find Fenton, his friend and 170 colleague. He found him by the coffee machine. Before he could ask him about Miller, Fenton spoke.

'Ah, Baker, you're back! What do you think of our new boss?'

'New boss?' What happened to Miller?' he asked. 175

'Miller? Don't you know? He's been promoted. Head Office gave him a sort of test – an imaginary case he had to solve. I think it gave him a bit of trouble, but he managed to find the answer in the end.

Baker's mouth hung open. [2] 180

'Don't look so surprised,' Fenton continued. 'Miller's a very intelligent man.'

---

1. **place** : position.
2. **hung open** : (to hang, hung, hung) expression made by face because of shock or surprise.

After reading

1 Answer these questions.

a. Why did Baker go to Miller's office?

....

b. Why did Cranberry go to the library?

....

c. What did he find in the book?

....

d. What took him to Madame Eve's?

....

e. How many times did he go to the cemetery?

....

f. When did Jenkins leave Cranberry?

....

2 Read the sentences below and decide which refer to Cranberry (C), Jenkins (J), Madame Eve (E) and Baker (B).

	C	J	E	B
a. It wasn't difficult at all.	☐	☐	☐	☐
b. I'll wait here, sir.	☐	☐	☐	☐
c. How much is it?	☐	☐	☐	☐
d. They're delivering the table tomorrow.	☐	☐	☐	☐
e. You've got a very beautiful house.	☐	☐	☐	☐
f. I'm sorry but she's very ill.	☐	☐	☐	☐
g. I can't find it anywhere.	☐	☐	☐	☐
h. I hid it in the bed.	☐	☐	☐	☐
i. Let's go skiing.	☐	☐	☐	☐
j. To the library, please.	☐	☐	☐	☐

3 Fill in the missing prepositions.

> into   in   for *(x2)*   of   on   up   at

a. Cranberry is leaving .... Cortina tomorrow.

b. The library is .... the end .... this road.

c. Jenkins waited .... Cranberry in the car.

d. The book was .... the top shelf. The librarian climbed .... the step-ladder to get it.

e. Did Cranberry believe .... the supernatural?

f. When Baker walked .... the room, Miller was waiting.

4 Match the words in column A with the correct synonyms in column B (refer to meaning in the story).

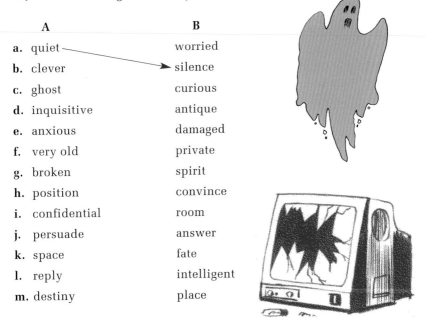

	A	B
a.	quiet	worried
b.	clever	silence
c.	ghost	curious
d.	inquisitive	antique
e.	anxious	damaged
f.	very old	private
g.	broken	spirit
h.	position	convince
i.	confidential	room
j.	persuade	answer
k.	space	fate
l.	reply	intelligent
m.	destiny	place

19

5 Match a sentence from column A with one in column B. Then join the sentences using the following words to make one sentence.

| because | so | and | but |

A	B
a. Miller asked Baker to solve the mystery.	He couldn't find the necklace.
b. Baker read the report.	He didn't go to the police.
c. Cranberry dug up his mother's grave.	His mother was very ill.
d. Jenkins left Cranberry.	He solved the mystery.
e. Cranberry had no proof.	He went on holiday.
f. Baker took some money out of the bank.	He didn't know why.
g. Cranberry wanted to go to the library.	He wanted promotion.

6 **A** Find words in the story that are the opposite of the following:

a. go out ....

b. calm ....

c. question (n) ....

d. finish ....

e. modern ....

f. close (v) ....

g. remember ....

h. win ....

i. full ....

j. light ....

k. well ....

B **Now complete the following sentences by using some of the opposites from 6A.**

a. I've always liked old furniture, how much is that .... chair?

b. It's really hot in here, can you .... the window?

c. Matthew had to take antibiotics when he was .... last month.

d. I'm not very lucky at playing cards, I always ....

e. Don't .... my birthday, it's tomorrow!

f. Don't stay outside in the rain, ... and get dry.

21

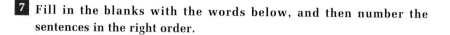

7 Fill in the blanks with the words below, and then number the sentences in the right order.

> handle   librarian   butler   receipt (x2)   pawnshop
> bought   library   grandmother's   address   visiting (x2)
> clairvoyant   past   luck   burying   mother's   night

☐ **a.** Cranberry woke up one morning and decided he wanted to go to the ....
He asked James, his .... to drive him there in the Rolls.

☐ **b.** Cranberry was amazed to discover that Madame Eve knew everything about his ...., his childhood, his girlfriends and his financial problems.

☐ **c.** When he arrived at the library, he went straight to the .... and asked her for a copy of *Strange Destiny*.

☐ **d.** She also told him that his .... could be changed only by .... his heirloom in his .... grave.

☐ **e.** The .... card had an .... in London that took him to see Madame Eve, a ....

☐ **f.** When he opened the book a .... fell out of it. It was from the local ....

☐ **g.** The .... of the mirror was loose and in it he found a .... card.

☐ **h.** Cranberry went straight to the pawnbroker, gave in the .... and .... a small, antique mirror.

☐ **i.** That .... Cranberry took his great .... diamond necklace and buried it in the cemetery.

22

ThE Penfriend

Before reading

1 Fill in the following application form about yourself.

Name ....

Address ....

Nationality ....

Age ....

School ....

How many languages do you speak? ....

Why are you studying English? ....

....

What do you like doing in your free time? ....

....

What kind of music do you like? ....

Have you ever had a penfriend? ....

From which country? ....

....

Give a brief description of who you would like to write to

(age, sex, nationality etc.) ....

....

....

....

....

2 One of the characters in the story is a teenager with problems.
Can you put her problems in order of importance for YOU!

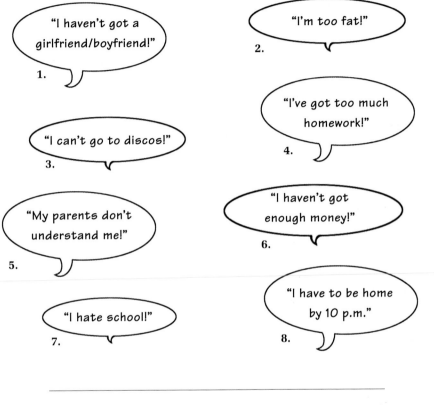

"I haven't got a girlfriend/boyfriend!"

1.

"I'm too fat!"

2.

"I've got too much homework!"

4.

"I can't go to discos!"

3.

"My parents don't understand me!"

5.

"I haven't got enough money!"

6.

"I hate school!"

7.

"I have to be home by 10 p.m."

8.

—   ORDER OF IMPORTANCE   +

Have you got any problems that aren't in the list? Write them in the space below.

....

....

....

....

The Penfriend

 rudy had argued [1] with her parents again. She couldn't stand it [2] anymore. She was old enough to look after herself! Every time she wanted to go out it was the same old story. [3]

5 They questioned her about where she was going, and who she was going out with. She felt that her parents didn't trust her at all. Things were getting worse and worse.

Tony had invited her to a party on Saturday night. When she told her parents about it, they said she could go but... she 10 had to be home by ten o'clock.

Her friends knew that her parents treated her like a child, and they often teased [4] her about it. Most of her friends had

1. **argued** : disagreed with each other.
2. **stand it** : tolerate the situation.
3. **the same old story** : the same questions again and again.
4. **teased** : made fun of.

26

THE Penfriend

really liberal parents and could do what they liked. She
sometimes thought about sharing a flat with her friend,
Sharon, but she knew it was only a dream. The money she   15
earned from babysitting wasn't even enough to buy herself
some new clothes.

If she didn't go to the party with Tony, he'd probably never
ask her out again. That's what usually happened. She got a lot
of invitations but she always refused. It was much easier saying   20
no than explaining why she had to be home by ten o'clock.

Trudy turned the music up louder and threw herself onto
the bed. She thought she could hear her mother shouting at
her to turn the music down, but she didn't care. She had lots
of homework to do, but couldn't be bothered. [1] Instead, she   25
opened a magazine and started looking through it when
something caught her eye. [2]

*'Are you depressed? Do you feel as though your life is not
your own? You're not alone. Please write to me. Susan'*

The address followed. Trudy was pleased to see she wasn't   30
the only one with problems. She found it difficult to talk to
her friends – they didn't understand her. Maybe this Susan
could give her some advice.

She sat up and reached for a pen and paper. It took her half
an hour to write a long letter. She wrote about her parents and   35

---

1. **couldn't be bothered** : didn't want to do it.
2. **caught** [kɔ:t] **her eye** : (to catch, caught, caught) attracted her attention.

ThE PenfrieNd

her problems in communicating with them, and also about
how she felt trapped.

When she had finished the letter she felt much better. She
posted it the next day.

A week later, she got a reply. It was a long letter from
Susan. As she read it Trudy realized that they both had many
things in common, apart from the fact that Susan had left
school. The last paragraph made Trudy realize that Susan's
problems were worse than hers.

> ... Things are getting unbearable. [1] They never speak to
> me, or ask my opinion about anything. I'm almost
> ignored. They don't really want me here. I heard
> them planning their holidays yesterday. They're thinking
> of going abroad and leaving me here on my own. [2] I don't
> know what to do...
> Write soon.
> Susan

Trudy felt sorry for her new friend. She wrote back the
same day.

1. **unbearable** : intolerable.
2. **on my own** : alone.

55 Dear Susan,

Thanks for your letter, and for your advice. You were right. It's much better trying to talk to my parents, than shouting and slamming [1] doors! I'm going to the party with Tony tonight but I have to be home by eleven.

60 It's not exactly what I wanted but it's better than nothing. What about your problems? Couldn't you go on holiday with them or speak to them? Tell them you don't want to stay at home on your own.

By the way, have you got a boyfriend?

65 Write soon and let me know.

Trudy

Things got better for Trudy. She learned how to explain things to her parents and they began to understand that she needed her freedom. At school she was doing well. She
70 studied hard and her results were always good.

While things got better for Trudy, they got worse for Susan. The next letter made Trudy very sad.

---

1. **slamming** : shutting doors violently.

ThE PenfrieNd

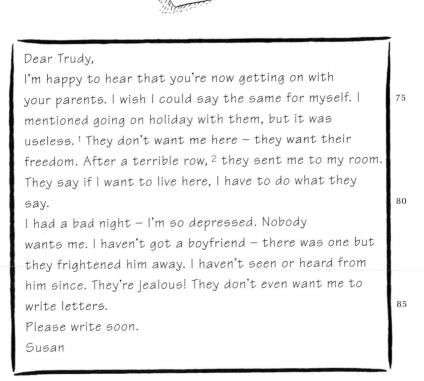

Dear Trudy,

I'm happy to hear that you're now getting on with
your parents. I wish I could say the same for myself. I
mentioned going on holiday with them, but it was
useless. [1] They don't want me here — they want their
freedom. After a terrible row, [2] they sent me to my room.
They say if I want to live here, I have to do what they
say.

I had a bad night — I'm so depressed. Nobody
wants me. I haven't got a boyfriend — there was one but
they frightened him away. I haven't seen or heard from
him since. They're jealous! They don't even want me to
write letters.

Please write soon.

Susan

Trudy wondered [3] what kind of parents the poor girl had.
Trudy started writing a reply immediately.

1. **useless** : had no positive results.
2. **row** [raʊ] : noisy and sometimes violent disagreement.
3. **wondered** ['wʌndəd] : asked herself.

90 Dear Susan,
I got your letter this morning. You're in a difficult
situation but don't forget that adults often say things
they don't mean. I'm sure they don't realize how
much they are hurting you. Tell them you're not a

95 child anymore – sending you to your room won't
solve anything!
I can understand them not wanting you to go out at
night (just like my parents!) but writing a few letters...
What harm can that do?

100 Things here are getting better. There's a concert next week
and they say I can go. I think they're beginning to like Tony!
Bye for now.
Trudy

Susan's reply came after a few days.

105 Dear Trudy,

I'm pleased things are improving for you – the situation here is getting worse! They went out for the day yesterday and wanted me to stay at home on my own. When I told them I wanted to go out they locked me in my

110 room. I can't stand it anymore – I feel really depressed. You're the only person I confide in. Now, they're refusing to post my letters so I give them to the boy who brings the newspapers. As for going out in the evenings, they won't even let me out during the day. I used to meet a

115 group of friends every Saturday but they stopped me going. Now I've lost contact with them all.

I know they wish I didn't exist, and sometimes, so do I.

Please write soon. Your letters are the only thing I look forward to. [1]

120 Susan

Trudy was shocked. Susan was being mentally tortured! She decided to show the letters to her parents.

'Oh, Trudy. You don't really believe everything that Susan writes, do you? It seems to me that she's got a very vivid

125 imagination,' her father said.

---

1. **look forward to** : wait for something with pleasure.

The Penfriend

'Write to her again,' her mother suggested. 'Invent something yourself. Play the same game.'

Trudy wasn't convinced. She wrote back the next day.

Dear Susan,
Are you on the phone?[1] Why don't you call the police? 130
What they're doing to you is a crime – they can't treat
you like this!
It's your life – you've got to change it now!
Please let me know what you decide to do.
Trudy 135

This time Susan took a while[2] to reply. The contents of the letter didn't surprise Trudy.

1. **Are you on the phone?** : Have you got a phone?
2. **a while** : a long time.

> Dear Trudy,
>
> Thanks for your advice – I appreciate you're trying to help me.
> I almost made the phone call you suggested but the more I
> thought about it, the more I decided against it. I know you
> find it hard to understand, but even though they treat me so
> badly, I still love them. If I call the police, or social services, [1]
> it'll create even more problems. Then, the police will arrest
> them. I'm not sure this is what I want. They're not too bad If
> I obey them...
>
> Please write soon.
>
> Susan

Trudy began to think that her parents were right. If Susan was really desperate, she would ask for help. She wrote back but didn't mention Susan's problems. Instead, she wrote about herself and Tony, and about life in general. This time she enclosed a photograph, and asked for one in exchange.

When Trudy received Susan's reply, she knew she had to do something.

---

1. **social services** : service provided by government to help people with problems.

The Penfriend

Dear Trudy,

Thanks for your photo. You sounded really happy in your letter. Things are a bit different here.

A few days ago I wanted to go out for a walk, but they wouldn't let me. I was so annoyed [1] I told them I was going to call the police. I've never seen them so angry, especially her. She slapped [2] me, and told me to go up to my room. As I was going up the stairs I slipped [3] and fell. I was a bit bruised, [4] but luckily didn't break any bones. I had to stay in bed for a day, but I'm much better now.

I'm sure they didn't mean to do it - but since then we haven't spoken. Maybe it's better, at least we don't argue! Hope to hear from you soon.

Susan

Trudy took the letter to her parents and insisted on phoning the police. Her mother had an idea. Her friend Maggie was a social worker. [5] She phoned her and explained the situation. Half an hour later, Maggie called at their house.

---

1. **annoyed** : angry.
2. **slapped** : hit across the face.
3. **slipped** : lost her balance.
4. **was a bit bruised** [bruːzd] : got some dark marks on the body caused by the fall.
5. **social worker** : (job) person who helps people with problems.

The Penfriend

She wanted to read the letters. When she'd seen them, she
told Trudy that she had done well to call her. Maggie
explained that a social worker would go and see Susan. She
promised to keep Trudy informed.

Trudy didn't write back to Susan. She preferred to wait and
hear from Maggie. Besides, she didn't know if Susan wanted to
write to her again, after what she had done.

One evening, Maggie came to visit them bringing them
news of Susan. It seemed that Susan had suffered physically
as well as mentally. At first, Susan would not admit that she
had been treated badly. When she saw the letters she had sent
Trudy, she agreed to tell the truth. After a brief stay in
hospital, the social worker found her somewhere to live. She
had given a letter to Maggie, for Trudy.

Dear Trudy,
At first I was upset [1] when I found out that you'd contacted
the social services. Now I understand why you did it. I'm
very happy here; the people I live with are very friendly and
kind.
I live quite near to you now — why don't you come and see me?
Hope to see you soon.
Susan

---

1. **upset** : unhappy.

A few days later, she took the train down to Hampton and then took a taxi to the address on the letter. A young girl answered the door. 'Susan's in the living room. She's waiting for you ...' When Trudy walked into the room, she thought
200   there had been a mistake. An old woman was sitting in an armchair reading a book. Trudy turned to leave, but the woman called her.

'You're Trudy, aren't you? I'm Susan,' she said, putting down her book.

205   'Susan?' Trudy answered perplexed. 'I thought...'

'Yes, I know. You thought you were writing to a young girl who had problems with her parents. Now you've discovered I'm an old woman who had problems with her son and wife.'

'Why didn't you tell me?' she asked.

210   'Because you didn't ask me,' Susan replied, laughing.
'I didn't lie to you, I just didn't mention a few details.'

'Yes, but why?'

'If you had known I was old enough to be your grandmother, would you have written to me?' Susan asked.

215   'I suppose not!' Trudy admitted.

'I enjoyed your letters so much. Young people are so full of life but think they're the only ones with problems... God only knows how many people there are in my situation. I was forced to live with a son who only wanted me for my pension.
220   After all I've done for him!'

ThE PenfrieNd

Susan and Trudy talked for a while. It was as though they had known each other for years.

As Trudy left the house she could see Susan in the garden chatting [1] away happily to her new friends. She decided to write to her the next day.

---

1. **chatting** : talking in a friendly manner.

After reading

1 **Are these sentences true (T) or false (F)?**

		T	F
a.	Trudy started to write to a penfriend because she was depressed.	☐	☐
b.	Susan didn't reply to the letter for a month.	☐	☐
c.	Trudy is going to a concert next week.	☐	☐
d.	Trudy wasn't doing very well at school.	☐	☐
e.	Susan hasn't got a boyfriend.	☐	☐
f.	Trudy received two photographs from her penfriend.	☐	☐
g.	Susan didn't call the police.	☐	☐
h.	When Susan saw the social worker she told the truth.	☐	☐
i.	Susan had problems with her mother and father.	☐	☐
j.	Trudy still writes to Susan.	☐	☐

Now correct the false sentences.

2 **Underline the correct word.**

"Susan's life sounded *great / awful*! When I received her last letter I was really *pleased / worried*. I wanted to call the *police / social worker* but my *mother / sister* stopped me. Instead I phoned a friend of my *mother's / father's* who came round straight away when she *heard / read* about the problem. I showed her the *photos / letters* and gave her Susan's *address / phone number*. I think somebody went round there the next *day / month*. Susan's *father / son* wasn't very happy when he saw her..."

3 Complete these sentences with the correct form of the verbs.

a. If Trudy .... (go) to the party, she'll have a good time.

b. If I .... (call) the police, they'll contact the social services.

c. The police will arrest them, if Trudy .... (tell) them about Susan.

d. If you .... (write) to a British penfriend, you'll improve your English.

e. If Trudy .... (not/go) to the party, Tony won't ask her again.

4 Here is a letter written by Susan to Trudy. Can you complete the gaps with the correct positive or negative forms of the verbs (Present Perfect or Past Simple)?

take   go   change   visit   live   write   be   catch   improve

Dear Trudy,

How are you? I'm sorry I .... to you for such a long time but I .... so busy since you .... me. By the way, thanks for the chocolates! My life .... completely - I .... here for two months now and I'm doing so many new things. I've started studying French and also doing some travelling. I .... to Paris last week for a couple of days - it was very exciting! We .... the ferry from Dover to Calais and then .... the train to Paris. I hope my French ....!

That's all for now. Please come and visit me if you have time.

Lots of love.

Susan

43

5 Look at these advertisements from the International Penfriends Association. Choose one of them and write a letter telling them about yourself, your interests, your dislikes etc.

British student, 18, wants to write in English to anybody in the world! Likes: Rock Concerts, travelling, Italian food. Dislikes: studying, discos and politics. Please write to:- Robert Walsh, 16 Whelan Drive, Cardiff

Australian unemployed teenager, 18, wants to write to students of English all over the world. Likes: swimming, surfing, reading, cooking, music and Italian girls! Dislikes: cars, noise, money. Write to:- Pete Salsa, 252 Spring Avenue, Sydney

American teenager, 16, from Texas, wants a penfriend in Europe (preferably male!)
Likes: Oasis, buying clothes, eating.
Dislikes: All sports!
Write to:- Kerry Lovack, P.O. Box 1642, Texas

6 **Look at these sentences:**

Trudy <u>has to</u> be home by 10 o'clock in the evening.
I <u>have to</u> stay in my room when my son goes out.

Can you complete the following sentences using the above structure?

a. I have to ....

b. My mother has to ....

c. Teachers ....

d. I don't ....

e. A politician ....

f. I ....

g. Students ....

7 **Do your parents understand you? Try the following quiz.**

a. What would your parents say if you wanted to go to a disco?
   ☐ Yes, if you come home early.
   ☐ No, you're too young.
   ☐ Yes, if we can come too!

b. If you wanted to go on holiday with your boyfriend/girlfriend, your parents would
   ☐ give you the money for the tickets.
   ☐ go with you.
   ☐ lock you in your room!

c. If you wanted a part-time job after school what job would your parents suggest?
   ☐ Babysitting.
   ☐ Working in a shop.
   ☐ Cleaning your bedroom!

45

d. How would your parents react if you wanted to go and share a flat with a friend?

- ☐ Buy you a flat and help you choose the furniture.
- ☐ Think you were mad.
- ☐ Stop you in some way!

e. What would you do if your parents decided to travel around the world and leave you at home?

If ....

I would ....

....

....

....

8 **Complete the following sentences:**

a. If I won a lot of money, I would ....

b. If I failed my exams, I would ....

c. If I were older, I ....

d. If my parents stopped me going to discos, I ....

e. If I left school, I ....

9 **Do you think old people are treated well in your country?**
Do you think old people should live with their families or be put into homes? Write a few sentences to express your opinion.

....

....

....

....

THE BiG MIstaKe

Before reading

1 **What kind of holiday do you like?**

a. What do you prefer...?
- [ ] The sea.
- [ ] The mountains.
- [ ] Cities.

b. What do you like doing?
- [ ] Going to discos.
- [ ] Reading books.
- [ ] Eating.
- [ ] Going sightseeing.

c. Who do you go on holiday with?
- [ ] With my friends.
- [ ] With my family.
- [ ] On my own.

d. How long do you go on holiday for?
- [ ] Less than a week.
- [ ] More than a week.
- [ ] More than a month.

e. How do you feel when you return?
- [ ] Happy and relaxed.
- [ ] Depressed.
- [ ] No different.

2 **A** **Match the definitions with the correct crime.**

a. Burglary   to enter a house with the intention of stealing

b. Murder   to steal from a bank

c. Theft   to take goods from a shop without paying

d. Robbery   to kill illegally

e. Shoplifting   to take away a person and ask for money in return

f. Kidnapping   to steal

B **Use your dictionary to find the names of the people who commit these crimes. One is done for you.**

Example   *burglary / **burglar***

....

....

....

....

....

ThE Big MistaKe

an James was really happy. The school year had
finished and the results of his exams were better
than expected. Now, after all those weeks of hard
work, he was going on holiday.

5 Fortunately, his rich uncle, Uncle Patrick, hadn't forgotten his
promise. Ian had spoken to him on the phone two nights
before – everything was planned. Uncle Patrick had left for
France so his house by the sea was empty. He'd left the fridge
full of food and drink and the key was under the doormat. 1

10 Ian could use the house until his uncle returned. Paula, his
girlfriend was coming to stay with him the next day and they
would be able to spend some time together.

He stared through the train window watching the houses,
fields and people go by. The train began to slow down as it

1. **doormat** :

50

ThE Big MIstaKe

came into Bridgeview Station.

The fat woman that sat opposite him was still asleep. The train stopped suddenly.

'Ooh,' she exclaimed, standing up and putting her head out of the window. 'It's Bridgeview.' She picked up her handbag and rushed to the door. 'It's lucky I woke up, otherwise I would have gone on to Littlepoint!'

So Ian knew he had to get off the train at the next station. He looked at his watch as the train left the station. Almost six o'clock. He was hungry and started thinking about all the food in the fridge that was waiting for him.

The scenery changed. In the distance he could see the sea and a few people on the beach. Ian had never been to his uncle's house before. He hadn't realized that he lived so close to the sea – he hoped it wasn't too polluted. [1]

He could smell the salty air of the sea.

The train hooted [2] as it approached the station of Littlepoint. Ian grabbed [3] his suitcase and got off the train. Luckily, there was a taxi free. He put his case in the boot and asked the driver to take him to Cliffview.

'What number?' the driver asked.

'Twenty eight,' Ian replied.

---

1. **polluted** : not clean.
2. **hooted** : made a short loud high sound.
3. **grabbed** : took suddenly.

ThE Big MIstaKe

It didn't take long to get there. The taxi stopped outside the largest house in the street.

Ian paid the taxi driver and picked up his case. As he walked up the path, he wondered who had planted all the flowers in the garden. He didn't think his uncle was the type to be interested in gardening. He continued up the path, and stopped at the door. He lifted up the doormat. The key was exactly where his Uncle Patrick had promised.

He opened the door and entered the hall, [1] closing the door behind him. He left his suitcase by the stairs, walked through the hallway and into the lounge. [2]

There were two long sofas in one corner of the room and a table and chairs occupied the centre. The floor was covered by a thick brown carpet and beige curtains hung at the windows. There was an enormous cabinet containing a lot of different ornaments, and a vase of flowers on the table.

Ian explored the rest of the ground floor. There was a bathroom, a dining room, a small study and a large kitchen.

Ian carried his suitcase upstairs. There were three bedrooms and a bathroom. He chose the biggest room and threw his case on the bed. He was too tired to unpack it. He went into the bathroom and had a quick shower. He left the towels on the floor and went to get dressed. He emptied his case, throwing his clothes on the chair. He would hang them

40

45

50

55

60

---

1. **hall** : the room in a house into which the front door opens.
2. **lounge** : living room.

up in the wardrobe later. Now he was hungry so he went downstairs to get some food. He opened the fridge – what a disappointment! There were two boiled potatoes, some ham and a bottle of milk. It wasn't much, but Ian had no choice. He
65 ate his meal in the lounge, in front of the television.

When he had finished he took the dishes into the kitchen and threw them into the sink. [1] He heard the plate break. When he returned to the lounge, his favourite quiz show was starting. He lay down on the sofa to watch television.

70 After a while, his eyes felt heavy. He was tired. He turned off the television and went upstairs to bed.

He had been asleep for about an hour, when he was awoken by a loud noise. A window being smashed! He heard the glass fall to the floor. He sat up in bed and switched on the bedside
75 lamp. He could hear voices from downstairs. Burglars!

He sat still for a moment, wondering what to do. The telephone was downstairs so he couldn't call for help. Should he go downstairs and face them? No... They may be dangerous.

He heard them walking through the hallway, and turning
80 on a light switch. Ian got out of bed and crept [2] onto the landing. [3]

He could hear the thieves talking – he listened to what they were saying.

---

1. **sink** : basin in the kitchen used for washing up.
2. **crept** : (to creep, crept, crept) moved slowly and quietly.
3. **landing** : area at the top of the stairs.

ThE Big MistaKe

'Where did you bury [1] him?'

'I think it's better if you don't know. Don't worry, nobody   85
will ever find him.'

'Oh God, I didn't mean to do it!'

Ian trembled. The thieves had killed someone and buried
the body.

He looked down the stairs and saw the two men. One of   90
them was sitting on the sofa, the other stood leaning against
the table. Both were wearing black suits. The man near the
table had a red stain on his white shirt. Blood!?

Ian walked as quietly as possible into the bedroom. He
closed the door behind him. How could he escape? [2]   95

He thought of a film that he had once seen. A man had
escaped from a burning house by using the bed sheets as a
rope. Ian ran to the window. He looked down. It was a long
drop. [3] There was no grass beneath him, just concrete.

Suddenly the voices were nearer. They were coming up the   100
stairs. Ian shook with fear. [4] He didn't know where to hide. He
looked around the room desperately. The wardrobe! He ran to
it, climbed inside, and pulled the door shut.

The voices and footsteps approached. Someone opened the
bedroom door – Ian stopped breathing. One of the men spoke.   105

---

1. **bury** : put under ground.
2. **escape** : get away.
3. **long drop** : long way to the ground.
4. **shook with fear** : (to shake, shook, shaken) was very frightened.

'I told you. There's nobody here. Look for yourself.'

They closed the door and continued along the landing.

Ian jumped out of the wardrobe and ran to the door – he opened it slowly. He checked that the landing was empty. The voices were coming from one of the larger bedrooms – they were looking for money!

Ian ran quickly out of the room and down the stairs – he had to call the police! He picked up the telephone and dialled 999. The phone was dead. [1] The murderers had cut the outside wires.

How could he call for help? He looked down at his bare feet. [2] His slippers were upstairs. So were his clothes. He couldn't go out into the cold night in his pyjamas!

The light on the landing suddenly came on. He could hear someone coming down the stairs. Ian threw himself onto the floor, behind the table. One of the men had gone into the kitchen. He heard him opening a cupboard, and pouring out a glass of water.

He had an idea. Now that the men had separated, maybe he could face them on his own. He moved as quietly as possible and hid behind the kitchen door. The man finished his drink and walked towards the hall. Ian was ready. Just as the man put his foot in the doorway, Ian pushed the door as hard as he

1. **The phone was dead** : The phone wasn't working.
2. **bare feet** : he had nothing on his feet.

could. The man shouted with pain and fell onto the floor. Ian
130 quickly closed the door and turned the key.

He knew that the man's cries would soon be heard by his
accomplice so he had to try and stop the other one. He didn't
have time to think. The man was coming down the stairs.

Ian crouched [1] down behind a cupboard. It was dark and he
135 couldn't be seen. The man lost his balance and fell down the
last few steps. Ian unplugged [2] the telephone and ran quickly
to where the man lay. He was face down and not fully
conscious. Using the telephone wire, Ian tied the man's hands
behind his back.

140 'Who are you? What do you want?' the man cried.

Ian didn't answer, and ran up the stairs to his bedroom. He
found his slippers [3] and his dressing gown. [4] Now he had to
run and get help.

He jumped over the man at the bottom of the stairs,
145 ignoring his cries, and ran towards the front door. He threw it
open and screamed with fright!

There before him was the man that he'd locked in the
kitchen! Blood was dripping from his nose. The man took hold
of Ian's arms and put them behind his back – he was very
150 strong. Ian couldn't escape!

1. **crouched** : made himself smaller by bending his knees.

2. **unplugged** : disconnected.

3. **slippers** :

4. **dressing gown** :

58

ThE Big MIstaKe

'You little hooligan! You forgot about the back door in the
kitchen, didn't you?'

He pushed Ian onto the sofa.

'Bill, untie me!'

The man that Ian had left at the bottom of the stairs stood   155
up and walked towards them. The telephone hung from the
wire behind his back.

'Who's this?' he asked.

'I don't know, but I'm going to teach him a lesson!'

He put his hand to the inside pocket of his jacket. He was   160
looking for his gun!

'Damn, I must have left it in the car,' the man said. He went
out of the front door.

Ian shook with fear. He looked around him. He had no
chance of escaping. The men were too big and too strong.   165
Maybe he could convince them to let him go.

'Listen,' he said, 'I've got some money upstairs in my case.
You can have it if you let me go. I won't tell anyone!'

'What?' the man laughed. 'You're joking!' [1]

The other man came back in. He was holding a small black   170
object. Ian closed his eyes. It was the end.

'No, no!' he begged. [2]

'Sorry. You deserve it,' came the reply.

Ian waited, his eyes still closed tightly.

---

1. **joking** : not serious.
2. **begged** : asked anxiously.

175 'Hello, police? I've just found a thief in my house. Yes, he's here in front of me.'

Ian opened his eyes in amazement. The little black object was a telephone!

'Your house?' he cried. They didn't answer him.

180 'The address? Twenty eight, Cliffview. Yes, he's under control. We'll wait.'

'What do you mean, your house? This is my uncle's house!'

'Try telling that to the police!'

Ian tried to convince them that he was telling the truth.

185 They wouldn't listen.

A few minutes later, a police car arrived. Ian was arrested.

At the police station he was questioned but nobody would believe him.

He was allowed to phone his uncle.

190 'Talk to them, Uncle Patrick. Tell them that the house is yours!'

His uncle's reply shocked him.

'I can't!' Uncle Patrick replied. 'It isn't my house. Mine is number twenty six!'

195 Uncle Patrick spoke to the police and explained the situation. Ian had made a terrible mistake!

'What about the man they buried? I heard them talking about the murder!' he said to the policeman.

The two men looked at each other.

200 'What man?' the policeman asked.

ThE Big MIstaKe

'That wasn't a man! It was a dog. We hit it with the car coming back from the restaurant. It didn't have a collar, it was a stray. 1 What else could I do?'

'And the blood on your shirt?'

'That's not blood!' the policeman replied. 'It's wine. I can smell it from here.' 205

Ian felt stupid. He had to stay in the station while the police and one of the men went to check that nothing had been stolen. When they returned, they had Ian's suitcase with them. It was almost eight o'clock in the morning. Ian was not 210 charged, and was free to go. He apologized to the two men, and was accompanied to his uncle's house. This time, the right one!

Ian was left in the doorway of twenty six, Cliffview. He'd had a bad night, and he was tired. He found the door key 215 under the mat. There was a letter under the door. He bent to pick it up. It was from Paula. It read:

> After three hours on the train, I expected to find you at home.
> Don't bother 2 phoning — I don't want to speak to you!

Ian had some explaining to do.

---

1. **stray** : animal without a home.
2. **Don't bother** : Don't worry about phoning.

After reading

1 Put these pictures into the order they appear in the story.
Then match the following actions with the pictures.

   a. arrive at house

   b. watch TV

   c. have shower

   d. go upstairs

   e. go to bed

   f. hear a noise

   g. tie the man's hands

   h. be arrested

☐ ☐

1 ☐

☐ ☐

☐ ☐

☐ ☐

☐ ☐

2 Put the sentences in Activity 1 into the past tense to write a summary of the story. Add other details to make the story more complete.

Example
Ian arrived at the house at 7 o'clock.

Use the following words to help you.

> bedroom TV and but because
> tired landing police downstairs

3 MEMORY QUIZ. **Do this quiz without looking at the story!**

a. Ian is going on holiday to
- ☐ Bigpoint.
- ☐ Littlepoint.
- ☐ Smallpoint.

b. What does Ian eat?
- ☐ Potatoes.
- ☐ Chicken.
- ☐ Rice.

c. The key was
- ☐ in the door.
- ☐ under the doormat.
- ☐ in a flowerpot.

d. Ian watched
- ☐ a soap opera.
- ☐ a quiz show.
- ☐ a documentary.

e. What did Ian forget in his room?
- ☐ His slippers.
- ☐ His book.
- ☐ His pyjamas.

f. Ian dialled
- ☐ 999.
- ☐ 666.
- ☐ 333.

g. Ian locked the thief in the
- ☐ kitchen.
- ☐ bathroom.
- ☐ toilet.

h. Uncle Patrick's house is at number

☐ 26.

☐ 27.

☐ 28.

i. What did the man have in his pocket?

☐ A knife.

☐ A gun.

☐ A mobile phone.

j. Ian offered the thieves

☐ some money.

☐ some tea.

☐ a gun.

k. The stray dog was

☐ in the road.

☐ in the field.

☐ in the house.

l. The stain on the man's shirt was

☐ blood.

☐ wine.

☐ tomato ketchup.

Now check your answers in the story.

4 Complete the puzzle.

1. Someone who steals.
2. An object which keeps things cold.
3. The top of a staircase.
4. Another name for 'living room'.
5. Clothes you usually wear in bed.
6. What you feel when somebody kicks you hard.
7. A place where you catch a train.
8. The telephone is connected to this.
9. Something you need to buy things.
10. Something you put flowers in.

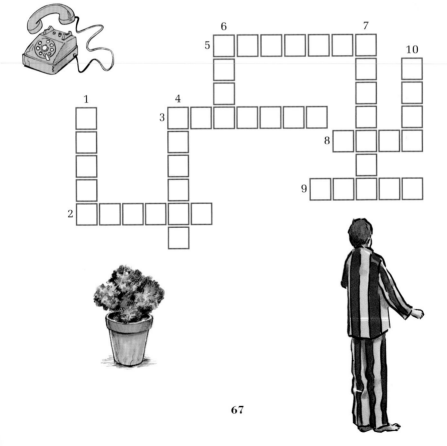

5 **Complete the sentences with question tags.**

Example: *You forgot about the kitchen door,* ***didn't you?***

a. The fridge is nearly empty, ...?

b. Ian got off the train at Littlepoint, ...?

c. He didn't eat much, ...?

d. Ian likes watching quiz shows, ...?

e. You're joking, ...?

f. The two men weren't thieves, ...?

g. That isn't blood, ...?

6 **Can you correct the mistakes in the following sentences?**

a. Ian came with the train yesterday.

....

b. Ian has arrived at Cliffview at about 6 o'clock.

....

c. Ian ate two boiled potato, a ham and drank a milk.

....

d. Ian tied the hands of the man.

....

e. The two men turned up the light.

....

f. Ian chose the most big room.

....

g. The thieves cutted the outside wires.

....

7 **Underline the correct preposition.**

a. Turn (in, up, off) the light before you go to bed.

b. Ian got (on, in, off) the train at Littlepoint.

c. The train slowed (up, down, up) just before the station.

d. The thief looked (for, at, in) the gun in his pocket.

e. Ian picked (up, off, out) his clothes and put them in the wardrobe.

f. It was so dark, he turned (off, on, out) the light.

8 **A Complete the spidergraph below.**

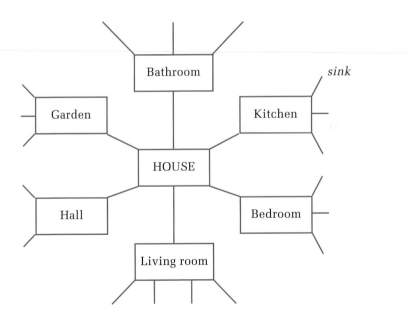

B Now complete these sentences.

a. You usually cook in the ....

b. Why don't you cut the .... in the garden?

c. I love watching .... in bed.

d. The .... in the bedroom is full of clothes.

e. British people usually hang up their coats in the

....

f. My mother used to wash clothes by hand, I prefer using a

..........................!

9 **Match the verbs in column A with the words in column B.**

A	B
a. You make	a train
b. You catch	television
c. You pick up	a shower
d. You look at	a mistake
e. You watch	clothes
f. You have	a suitcase
g. You hang up	the light
h. You switch on	a watch

10 **Can you think of another ending to the story? Write a few lines below.**

....

....

....

Listening

1 **Listen to the first part of the story and correct the mistakes, if necessary.**

a. Ian had passed his exams.

....

b. Ian was going on holiday to the mountains.

....

c. His girlfriend Paula was arriving the next day.

....

d. Ian got off the train at Bridgeview.

....

e. He waited for a bus outside the station.

....

f. The ground floor had five rooms.

....

g. Ian went upstairs, took his clothes off and had a bath.

....

h. There wasn't much food in the fridge.

....

i. Ian ate his meal in the kitchen, in front of the television.

....

Now check your answers in the text.

2 While listening to the story tick (✓) the objects which are NOT mentioned.

a ☐

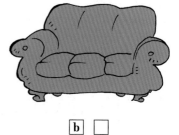

b ☐

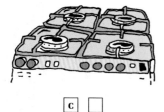

c ☐

d ☐

e ☐

f ☐

g ☐

h ☐

Marge and Olive

Before reading

1 **What do you do at home?**

	always	often	never
• do the shopping	☐	☐	☐
• do the washing up	☐	☐	☐
• do the cleaning	☐	☐	☐
• do the cooking	☐	☐	☐
• do the ironing	☐	☐	☐
• make the beds	☐	☐	☐
• put the rubbish out	☐	☐	☐
• lay the table	☐	☐	☐

What do you like doing the most? ....

What do you like doing the least? ....

2 **Underline the word that is different. Why is it different?**

a. beef   lamb   cow   chicken   pork

b. eggs   yoghurt   milk   coffee   cream

c. pasta   flour   rice   bread   beans

d. tea   milk   cornflakes   juice   coca-cola

e. apple   pineapple   grapes   pepper   melon

f. potato   cucumber   tomato   lettuce   cherry

3 **What do you think this story is about? Read the beginning of the story (lines 1-7) to help you.**

• crime   • love   • horror   • adventure   • war

Now read the story to check your answer.

MArge aNd OLiVe

marge and Olive were two sisters who had lived together all their lives. They were both over seventy. When their father died leaving them the house and some money, it was Olive who was the boss. She was a little older than Marge and had a very bad temper. Marge was afraid of her, and soon learnt to do everything she was told to do. Olive did the shopping, paid the electricity, gas and water bills, and decided how to spend their money. Marge did the cleaning, the cooking and decided when to put the rubbish [1] out to be collected.

Marge hadn't been shopping for a long time; she couldn't walk far because of her arthritis. Besides, it wasn't necessary for her to go shopping – Olive was happy to go on her own.

5

---

1. **rubbish** : unwanted things that people throw away (here, empty food packets, bottles, paper etc.).

Marge hated shopping days. Olive arrived home carrying
15 the heavy bags – always in a terrible mood [1] – and ordered
Marge to make her a cup of tea. Then Marge would go and get
Olive's slippers. [2] Olive would then start complaining and say
that Marge was lucky to have someone to do the shopping for
her. Marge nodded [3] silently. She knew it was better not to
20 argue with Olive. As Marge unpacked the shopping, putting
everything in the cupboards, Olive talked about the price of
things. Especially clothes. They were so expensive! That is
why they had to share them, or more exactly, Marge would
have Olive's old clothes.

25 Marge often asked her sister to buy her certain foods she
liked. Olive would always refuse, because she couldn't eat
these things herself. Cheese, milk and yoghurt would give her
terrible stomach pains. So Marge was left without.

Marge had a really difficult time when Olive was ill. She
30 would often have to get out of bed, late at night, to give Olive
a tablet for her angina. [4] Sometimes, Olive would wake her up
just because she wanted a cup of tea. Marge would always
obey. She didn't have the courage to refuse, and by now, she
was used to being treated badly. Besides, she had a secret that
35 helped her to put up with [5] Olive. Alfred was back!

---

1. **mood** : state of mind.
2. **slippers** :
3. **nodded** : moved her head up and down to show agreement.
4. **angina** [æn,dʒaɪnə] : illness of the heart.
5. **put up with** : tolerate.

When Marge was much younger, Alfred had been her boyfriend, and they had planned to get married. Olive was really jealous and had done everything possible to separate the two. When she discovered that Alfred had been accused of
40 being a deserter [1] during the Second World War, she had told her father. Alfred had tried to explain that it had all been a mistake, but their father would not listen. He sent Alfred away, and ordered Marge not to see him again. Alfred left the town and later Marge heard that he had married someone else.
45 It took her a long time to forget him. She hated Olive for this and would never forgive her. [2]

Now, after all these years, Alfred had moved back into town. He had lost his wife a few years before, and had written to Marge asking her to forgive him. He was aware of the
50 terrible life that Marge had with her domineering sister, and he felt responsible. In his first letter he told Marge how he wished that he had had the courage to explain to her father, instead of leaving her. He had been a coward. [3]

Marge was so pleased to receive his letter, that she forgave
55 him instantly. She wrote back and they began to write regularly. When Olive found out that Alfred had returned she tried to stop Marge writing to him. Marge ignored her and even managed to meet Alfred on the days when Olive went

---

1. **deserter** : person who leaves military service without permission.
2. **never forgive her** : never forget what Marge had done.
3. **coward** : person who is afraid to face things.

Marge and Olive

shopping. They discovered that, despite their age, [1] and the
years that had passed, there was still something special   60
between them. Marge knew that if Olive discovered their
meetings, she would never see Alfred again. The thought of
this was terrible. Since Alfred had returned she had begun to
live again. They talked about lost friends, the dance halls that
they had danced in, and the wonderful music of the old days.   65
Sometimes they would sing together. Alfred would often bring
her chocolates, sweets and even the cream and yoghurt she
adored. For the first time after so many years, Marge felt
wanted. It was the only thing that helped her through the day,
and she wasn't prepared to lose Alfred again.   70

Even though they met occasionally, they decided that it
was better to keep writing to each other. Olive would be
suspicious if Marge stopped receiving letters. She'd miss
them, too. Olive would always read Marge's letters. She would
say she had a headache, and that she would go upstairs to lie   75
down. [2] But Marge knew it was just an excuse. She had tried
hiding [3] them but it was no use. Olive still found them.

At their last meeting, Alfred had asked her to marry him.
She had accepted, but what about Olive? Marge had thought
about leaving home, but this meant that she'd lose all her   80

---

1. **despite their age** : even though they were old.
2. **lie down** : have a rest on the bed.
3. **hiding** : (to hide, hid, hidden) putting the letters in a place which was difficult to find.

money. Olive kept the bank books in her name. No, it was
Olive that would have to go!

The next evening, Marge and Alfred met at the same time,
at the same place. They talked about Olive and Alfred told
85 Marge about a plan that would finally solve everything. Marge
listened carefully. Alfred was a genius! She was sure that the
plan would work, and soon they would be free. Alfred gave
her a small tin [1] and a letter. He told her to be very careful,
and to make sure that Olive did not find them. Marge hid them
90 in her handbag. She could not wait, so they decided to carry
out the plan the very next day.

Marge slept well that night. When Olive came downstairs
for breakfast, she sang cheerfully to herself. Olive told her to
shut up immediately, and complained that her tea was cold.
95   'The postman has already been,' Marge said, as she fried
the eggs.

'So what?' Olive answered.

'There was just one letter – for me,' Marge replied.

Olive smiled. Good, she thought. Something for her to read
100 later on. Marge put the fried egg on Olive's plate.

'What shall we have for lunch today?' Marge asked.

'This egg is overcooked. Give me the other one!' Olive
ordered.

Marge obeyed, and said once again, 'What shall we ...'

1. **tin** : small metal container.

Marge and Olive

'I heard you the first time. I'm not deaf!'   105

Marge jumped. She always did when Olive shouted.

'Meatloaf!' Olive continued. 'We always have meatloaf on Tuesday. And don't ask stupid questions!'

Marge nodded. They carried on eating their breakfast in silence.   110

Afterwards, Olive went into the garden to read the newspaper. Marge did her housework, then began to prepare the meatloaf. When she'd mixed the ingredients together, she went to her handbag and found the small tin. She opened it and added the contents to the mixture. She mixed it in   115 quickly, and hid the empty tin in the washing machine. Then she put the meatloaf in the oven to cook, and tried not to act suspiciously.

When the meatloaf was cooked, Marge sniffed at it. She could not smell anything unusual. She was not hungry though.   120 She told Olive that she had a headache, and that she did not want to eat. Olive was not particularly worried and started eating. Marge watched her from behind the kitchen door. That day, Olive ate more than usual.

After lunch, Marge did the washing up and Olive went to   125 her room to lie down. Marge knew that she would read the letter. Things were going exactly as planned.

Olive rushed into Marge's room, found the letter, then returned to her own room to read it.

130 | Dear Marge,

The small tin that you found at the bottom of your garden is a very strong poison that I bought for the mice in my cellar. [1]

You were right, my dear, it's the only way to get rid of [2] Olive. Put it in the meatloaf that you mentioned.

135 | She won't notice the taste or smell! The effect is almost immediate.

Please be patient,

All my love

Alfred

140   Olive read the letter quickly, then she read it again, stopping at the word – poison. She threw the letter down, and suddenly felt hot. An unbearable pain began in her stomach, and she cried out.

    'Oh, my God! I've been poisoned. Help!'

145   Marge heard her from downstairs. She turned the volume of the radio up and ignored her.

    The pain got worse and Olive fell to the floor, trying to breathe. How long would it take? Was she dying? Yes, the letter had said that the poison was very strong! She lay on the

150 carpet waiting for someone to help her. She felt another pain, much stronger than the other, in her chest. [3] Her left arm

---

1. **cellar** : room underground used for storing wine etc.
2. **get rid of** : become free of.
3. **chest** : top front part of the body.

ached. It was her heart. She was having an attack. Where were her tablets? She called for Marge.

Marge sang to herself and waited. After a while, she could no longer hear Olive calling for her. She picked up the   155
telephone and called for an ambulance.

When it arrived, Olive was dead. Marge cried as they took her away, but she cried tears of joy. [1] The doctor signed the death certificate. Olive had died of a heart attack; there was no mention of poison.   160

Alfred and Marge were married a few months after Olive's death. They often talked about how they got rid of Olive, especially after their bedtime drink. The small tin of poison was given a place on the kitchen shelf, where its label [2] could be seen by all.

It read, 'Concentrated Powdered Milk'.

1. **joy** : happiness.
2. **label** : piece of paper on the tin that described the contents.

After reading

1 **What can you remember about the story? Don't check your answers until you have finished answering all the questions!**

a. Marge and Olive's age ....

b. The eldest sister ....

c. Marge's illness ....

d. Marge's favourite food ....

e. Marge and Alfred's secret meeting place ....

f. What Alfred and Marge talked about ....

g. The presents Alfred bought ....

h. What the sisters had for breakfast ....

i. Why Marge didn't eat that evening ....

j. How Olive died ....

k. When Alfred and Marge got married ....

l. What was put on the kitchen shelf ....

2 **Who/what do the underlined words refer to?**

a. When <u>their</u> father died.

b. Marge was afraid of <u>her</u>.

c. <u>They</u> were so expensive.

d. She couldn't eat <u>these things</u>.

e. <u>It</u> had all been a mistake.

f. She'd miss <u>them</u> too.

g. Olive did not find <u>them</u>.

h. Give me the other <u>one</u>.

i. When <u>it</u> arrived ...

j. <u>It</u> read ...

3 **Rearrange the words to make complete sentences.**

a. before Second met the Alfred War World Marge

....

b. letters Olive read Marge's always

....

c. left money a Olive's and father Marge lot of

....

d. had desertion accused been of Alfred

....

e. handbag hid Marge the in tin letter her the and

....

f. Marge ambulance and telephone picked an called up the

....

4 **How good is your vocabulary? Choose the correct definitions.**

1. temper
   a. anger
   b. a pencil
   c. a river

2. a mistake
   a. a headache
   b. an error
   c. a cake

3. a genius
   a. a character in Aladin
   b. a very clever person
   c. a banknote

4. a meatloaf
   a. bread
   b. a dish made of meat
   c. a sweet

5. to sniff
   a. to have a cold
   b. to smell
   c. to taste

6. angina
   a. a flower
   b. a dance
   c. an illness

7. tin
   a. a small car
   b. a container made of metal
   c. a toy

8. cellar
   a. salt
   b. a room underground
   c. a bird

9. to sign
   a. to write your name
   b. to draw
   c. to sing a song

10. a tablet
   a. a pill
   b. a type of table
   c. a blackboard

11. price
   a. sound
   b. cost
   c. fruit

12. poison
   a. a drink
   b. food
   c. a very dangerous substance

5 Complete the sentences with the words in the box.

than   to   for   of (x2)   on   about

a. Marge was afraid .... Olive.

b. Olive was a little bit older .... Marge.

c. Olive liked going shopping .... her own.

d. Olive often talked .... the price of clothes.

e. Alfred asked Marge .... marry him.

f. Olive ordered Marge to make her a cup .... tea.

g. After a while Marge called .... an ambulance.

6 Here is a page from Marge's diary. There are 10 grammatical mistakes in it – can you correct them?

MONDAY **22** September

At last Alfred and J is happy! Olive dead last month and we had his funeral a week later. Now Alfred and J can get marry. We goed into town yesterday to do some shopping – J bought meself a beautiful pink dress and Alfred buyed some new shoes. We hope to get married in a few month time and then go to the seaside for ours honeymoon. J sometimes miss Olive and her strange ways but J think J prefer to live with Alfred – he love me so much ...

1. ....
2. ....
3. ....
4. ....
5. ....
6. ....
7. ....
8. ....
9. ....
10. ....

Listening

1 Who did what? Olive (O), Marge (M) or Alfred (A).
Listen to the story and then without looking at the
text tick (✓) accordingly:

	O	M	A
a. paid the bills	☐	☐	☐
b. got the slippers	☐	☐	☐
c. made the tea	☐	☐	☐
d. left the town	☐	☐	☐
e. sang together	☐	☐	☐
f. made breakfast	☐	☐	☐
g. bought the poison	☐	☐	☐
h. took tablets	☐	☐	☐

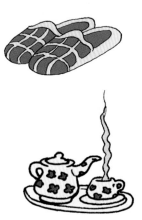

Now listen again and check your answers.

2 Listen to the first part of the story and fill in the following gaps.

Marge and Olive were two sisters who .... lived together all
.... lives. They were both .... seventy. When their father
died leaving .... the house and some money, it was Olive who
was the boss. She was a .... older than Marge and had a very
bad .... Marge was afraid of her, and soon .... to do
everything she was told to do. Olive did the shopping, paid the
.............., gas and water bills, and decided how to spend their
money. Marge did the ...., the cooking and decided when to
put the .... out to be collected.

Simpson's Buried Treasure

Before reading

1 **Answer the following questions:**

- Have you ever found any money?

  ....

- Where did you find it?

  ....

- How much did you find?

  ....

- Have you ever found anything strange or unusual?

  ....

2 **Which word is the odd one out? Why?**

a. grass   tree   lawn   spade

....

b. rain   thunder   sun   hot

....

c. stupid   strong   cry   heavy

....

3 **Look through the first part of the story (lines 1-10) quickly and find the following information:**

a. How many boys are there?

....

b. What are their names?

....

c. Where are they at the beginning of the story?

....

Simpson's Buried

TreasurE

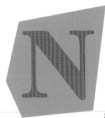 Nicholas walked slowly down the narrow country road holding the dirty piece of paper tightly [1] in his hand. In the distance he could see Buster standing against the wall, smoking a cigarette. Nicholas was frightened. He knew he was in Buster's territory and that Buster would probably hit him for being there. As usual, Buster was not alone. Lewis and Driscoll, two of his closest friends, stood waiting for orders. Nicholas knew he was in trouble. Buster always wanted to show that he was the boss.

'Look, there's Rabbit!'

Nicholas stopped suddenly as the three boys ran towards him. Buster threw down his cigarette. He blew the last of the smoke into Nicholas's face.

---

1. **tightly** : firmly.

15 'Are you deaf, or just stupid, eh Rabbit?'

Nicholas coughed as the disgusting smoke filled his nostrils. 1 He felt a sudden blow 2 to the side of his face. His cheek hurt and he wanted to cry but he made himself stop.

'You're trespassing, 3 Rabbit!' Driscoll continued. I've told
20 you to keep away from here.'

The boys surrounded him, and a heavy hand pushed him to the ground. Nicholas covered his head with his arms and closed his eyes, waiting for the blows.

'What's this?'
25 'Looks like a map.'

'That's old Simpson's garden!'

'Yeah! But what are all those crosses for?'

Nicholas opened his eyes and lifted his head. Buster was holding the piece of paper he had dropped.
30 'Hey Rabbit! Whose map is this? What's it for?' Buster grabbed Nicholas by the arm, and pulled him up. Nicholas kept his head down and didn't answer.

'Come on, tell me before I...!' Buster pushed Nicholas against the wall.
35 'Okay, okay! It's a map of Simpson's garden,' he answered reluctantly.

---

1. **nostrils** :
2. **blow** : hard stroke (given with a hand/stick).
3. **trespassing** : entering private property without permission.

SimPson's Buried TreasurE

'I can see that, you idiot. What are you doing with it?'

Once again Nicholas refused to speak. The three bullies [1] stood over him, and he knew that they were waiting for an answer. 40

'It's a map of Simpson's buried treasure, but it's only a legend. Nobody believes that it really exists,' he said.

'Ah, no. Then where were you going?' Lewis replied.

'Yeah! That's why you had the nerve to pass through here! You're hoping to find the treasure yourself. 45

'I've heard about that treasure,' added Driscoll. 'They say that old Simpson buried a fortune in his garden before he died.'

'Oh, no! It's only a legend. Nobody really believes that story'. Another blow made Nicholas fall to the ground. His 50 arm ached. [2]

'Shut up! I'll be the judge of that!' Buster said, smiling to the others. 'Now, get lost!' [3]

Nicholas stood up and moved away.

'Go on, run!' Lewis yelled, [4] laughing. 55

Nicholas ran as fast as he could. Laughter and cries of 'run rabbit run' came from behind him.

Once he'd turned the corner, he stopped to catch his

---

1. **bullies** : (singular: "bully") people who hurt or frighten weaker people.
2. **ached** : hurt.
3. **get lost** : go away.
4. **yelled** : shouted loudly.

breath, and waited. As expected, the three boys were walking
60 towards old Simpson's house chatting [1] together excitedly.
They didn't know that Nicholas was following them!

When the small group entered the garden, Nicholas crept [2]
into a large hole in the hedge of the house next door. Here, he
could watch the boys without the risk of being discovered.

65 'Oh no!' Buster exclaimed, his face falling. The garden was
really overgrown with grass and weeds [3] everywhere.

'How can we dig for treasure if we can't see where we are
digging?' Lewis asked, kicking at some weeds.

'We'll have to cut the grass first,' Buster announced.
70 'You two go and get some gardening tools and a
lawn mower. Don't forget the spades.' [4]

Lewis and Driscoll disappeared and
left Buster alone in the garden.
Nicholas knelt down to rest his
75 tired legs, and prepared himself
for a long wait. The wind blew
through the hedge, and a large
grey cloud blocked out the last rays of
the sun. He looked up and realized that it was going to rain.

---

1. **chatting** : talking in a friendly manner.
2. **crept** : (to creep, crept, crept) moved slowly and quietly.
3. **weeds** : wild plants growing where not wanted.
4. **spades** :

80 'Come on!' Buster exclaimed, as the two boys struggled [1] through the wooden gate with their equipment. 'I'll start mowing, you two can clear up [2] the grass,' he ordered, pushing the heavy mower onto the untidy lawn.

Nicholas watched patiently as the bullies worked. The
85 rhythmic sound of the lawn mower, and the sweet smell of freshly cut grass was quite pleasant.

The first drops of rain made them work faster, and they hardly spoke as they carried on working.

'Leave the grass over there in the corner.' Buster shouted
90 over the noise of the howling [3] wind. 'Hurry up! There's going to be a storm.'

He had hardly finished the sentence, when a loud noise startled [4] all four of them – thunder! [5] Large drops of rain fell heavily, soaking them to the skin [6] instantly. All except
95 Nicholas. The thick hedge provided an excellent shelter, [7] and he enjoyed watching the three boys struggling with their spades, and following the instructions on the map.

'Have you found anything?' Lewis shouted, wiping his face with a damp sleeve.

---

1. **struggled** : had difficulty carrying the tools.
2. **clear up** : tidy up.
3. **howling** : blowing hard, making a loud noise.
4. **startled** : frightened.
5. **thunder** : loud sound in the sky during a storm.
6. **soaking them to the skin** : making them very, very wet.
7. **shelter** : cover.

SimPson's Buried TreasurE

'No! What about you, Driscoll?' Buster replied.   100

'Nothing, and I've dug three holes already! I'm really wet!'

'Me too!'

The wet earth became heavier by the minute and Buster
was getting tired.

'This stupid spade won't come out of the mud,' he cried.   105
He was getting angrier and angrier. To the relief of his friends,
he shouted, 'Let's get out of here! It's obvious that the treasure
doesn't exist!'

As he turned to go, he stumbled [1] over one of the holes that
he'd dug.   110

'Aaargh!'

Nicholas covered his mouth with his hand. The sight of
Buster lying on the ground with his face covered with mud
was more than he'd expected. He started laughing
uncontrollably. He knew that he couldn't be heard above the   115
noise of the rain.

He watched as the boys, arguing amongst themselves,
collected up their tools, and left the garden. Nicholas couldn't
stop laughing.

As suddenly as it had started, the rain stopped. Nicholas   120
crawled [2] out of his hiding place. He looked round the garden.
It was wet, but very tidy. In his haste, [3] Buster had forgotten

---

1. **stumbled** : fell.
2. **crawled** : moved slowly on his hands and knees.
3. **In his haste** : In the hurry.

his spade and had left it sticking out of the ground. Nicholas
jumped over the hedge to get it, then ran to the front of the
125   house and waited.

Finally, the grey clouds disappeared, and the sun came out.
A blue car which Nicholas recognized immediately,
approached slowly, stopping outside old Simpson's house.
The driver, a tall, smart woman with red hair, stepped out of
130   the car and walked towards him.

'Nicholas', she called, looking at the muddy spade and
smiling. 'Don't tell me that you've already done that job we
talked about? You haven't tidied up the garden already, have
you?'

135   'Yes, Miss Simpson,' Nicholas replied, wiping his forehead
and sighing. The woman walked around to the back of the
garden.

'Good Lord![1] What a wonderful job you've done! And in the
rain, too. You poor thing,' she continued, putting a hand on
140   his shoulder. 'And you've even dug the holes for my rose
bushes, exactly where I wanted them!' she exclaimed.

Without hesitation she put her hand into her shoulder bag,
and pulled out a small purse.

'Let me pay you at once. I didn't expect you to do such a
145   good job. And all on your own, too!'

---

1.   **Good Lord!** : expression of surprise.

Simpson's Buried Treasure

She took out one, two, then three £5 notes from her purse. Nicholas gasped. [1]

'But Miss Simpson...' he pretended to be surprised.

'Oh, no. I insist. Take it, you've done a very good job.'

Thanking her again and again, Nicholas accepted the money and turned to go home. He knew that he would have to avoid [2] Buster for a while. Fortunately for him, a bad cold would keep Buster out of the way for a long time.

---

1. **gasped** : took in his breath suddenly because of surprise.
2. **avoid** : keep away from.

After reading

1 Are the following sentences true (T) or false (F)?

		T	F
a.	Nicholas met the boys in Simpson's garden.	☐	☐
b.	Buster was with two of his friends.	☐	☐
c.	Buster was the leader.	☐	☐
d.	Buster hit Nicholas three times.	☐	☐
e.	There was a rabbit running in the field.	☐	☐
f.	Nicholas hid in the house.	☐	☐
g.	The boys cleaned the garden before digging.	☐	☐
h.	Buster found the treasure.	☐	☐
i.	Miss Simpson owned the garden.	☐	☐
j.	Miss Simpson paid Nicholas for watching the boys.	☐	☐

Now correct the false sentences.

....

....

....

....

....

....

....

2 A The pictures below are scenes from the story – but they are all mixed up. Can you put them into the correct order? (Don't complete the sentences yet!)

a ☐

The boys .... into the garden.

b ☐

Buster and friends .... working.

c ☐

Nicholas .... Buster and his friends.

d ☐

Miss Simpson .... Nicholas some money.

e ☐

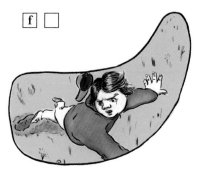

Buster .... Nicholas across the face.

f ☐

It started raining and Buster .... into a hole.

g ☐

The boys .... the garden.

h ☐

Nicholas .... behind a hedge.

i ☐

Miss Simpson .... in her car.

B Now put the correct form of the verbs (Simple Past) into the gaps.

> meet   hit   go   hide   start   fall   leave   arrive   give

3 Can you match the words with the correct definition? (All the words are in the story.)

a. stupid   part of the body

b. legend   shout loudly

c. spade   not very intelligent

d. stumble   a very old story

e. wet   a tool used for digging

f. yell   not dry

g. face   fall over

4 **A** All these things are usually found in the garden or in the countryside. Can you solve the anagrams? Use the pictures to help you.

a. deesw ....

b. olto ....

c. omewlarnw ....

d. despa ....

e. gedhe ....

f. ragss ....

g. busrhsoe ....

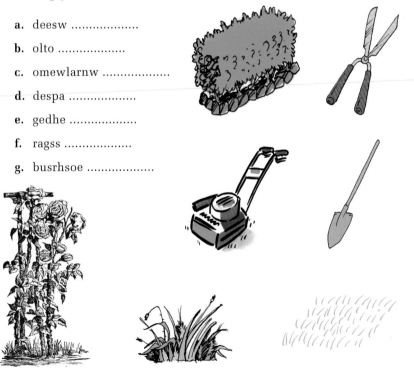

B **Now can you find them in this word grid?**

G	D	R	R	S	T	Z	H	K
L	A	W	N	M	O	W	E	R
T	R	E	E	L	O	E	D	H
M	D	G	P	P	L	E	G	Q
U	X	R	S	P	A	D	E	V
D	Y	A	F	D	E	S	O	O
Y	U	S	Q	P	U	I	C	H
R	O	S	E	B	U	S	H	J

5 **A** **Complete the chart below.**

a. Tall	Taller	Tallest
b. Cold	....	....
c. Young	....	....
d. Rich	....	....
e. Fat	....	....
f. Hot	....	....
g. Wet	....	....
h. Thin	....	....
i. Happy	....	....
j. Small	....	....
k. Good	....	....
l. Bad	....	....
m. Intelligent	....	....
n. Beautiful	....	....

B Now using the adjectives from 5A, write a sentence about each boy using the superlative. The pictures will help you.

a. Buster always eats lots of cakes, sweets and chocolate.

He's ....

b. Nicholas has got a lot of money.

He's ....

c. Buster is 1m 65, Driscoll is 1m 63 and Lewis is 1m 70.

Lewis is ....

d. Driscoll looks younger than his age because he's not very tall.

....

6 This is a map of the country village where the boys live. Read the directions on the next page and put the symbols from the key in the places on the map.

Go straight up the road. Take the second road on the left – there's a chemists' on the corner. Go down this road until you come to the bridge. Take the first left after the bridge. When you come to a pub called 'The Cock and Bull' turn right and then second left. At the end of this road turn left again. After about 200 metres you'll come to some traffic lights. Nicholas lives in the house on the right after the traffic lights.

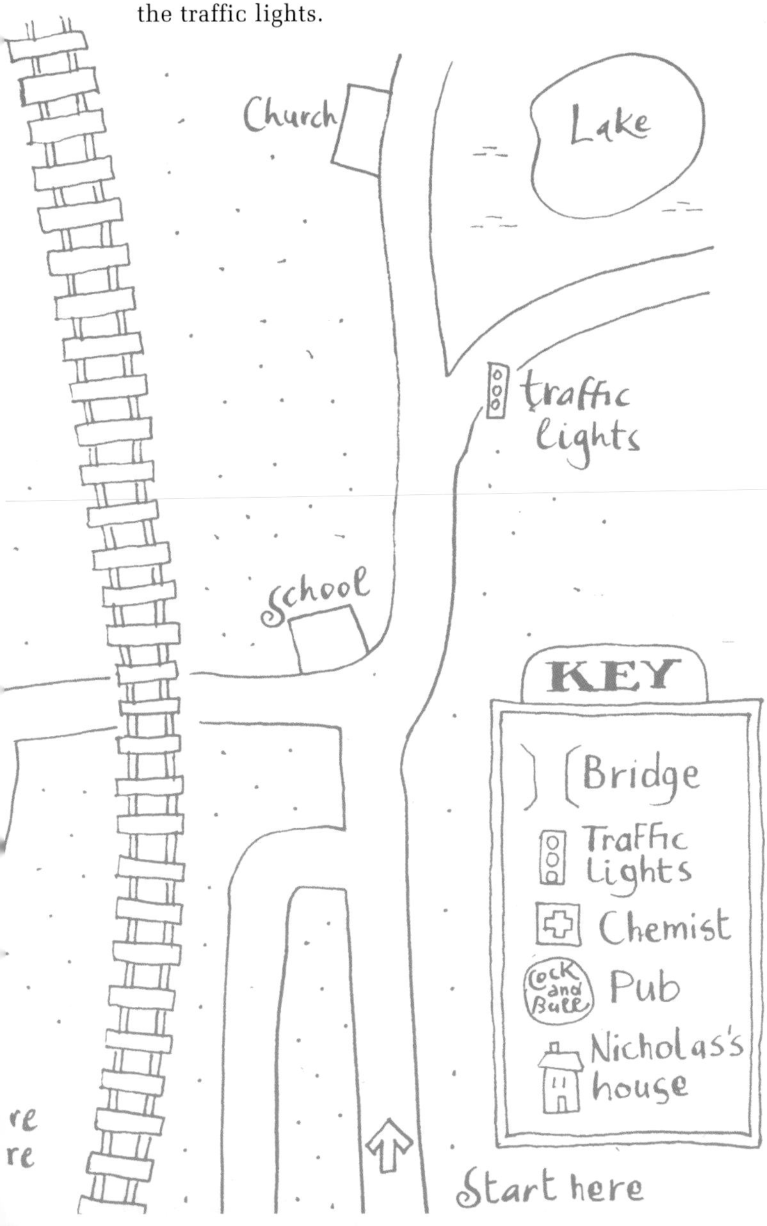

Church

Lake

traffic
lights

School

KEY

) (Bridge

Traffic
Lights

Chemist

Pub

Nicholas's
house

Start here

7 **Complete the following clues.**

   a. Longest part of the body ....

   b. You write with this ....

   c. It's in the middle of your face ....

   d. They can be blue, green or brown ....

   e. You eat, speak and kiss with this ....

   f. We usually have 32 ....

   g. The plural form is irregular ....

   h. You hear with these ....

   i. The top part of the body ....

   j. It joins the head to the body ....

   k. Part of face above eyebrows ....

   l. Your arms are attached to these ....

Use your dictionary to find other parts of the body you don't know.

....

....

....

....

....

....

Listening

4 **1** **Read the following questions. Then try and find the answers by listening to the story.**

a. What was Nicholas holding?
- [ ] a cigarette
- [ ] a map
- [ ] a book

b. Where was Nicholas hiding?
- [ ] in a hedge
- [ ] in a house
- [ ] in a hut

c. The leader's name was
- [ ] Bunter
- [ ] Buster
- [ ] Butter

c. What did the boys find?
- [ ] some money
- [ ] some gold
- [ ] nothing

d. The weather that day was
- [ ] foggy
- [ ] sunny
- [ ] windy

e. How much did Miss Simpson pay Nicholas?
- [ ] £ 5
- [ ] £ 10
- [ ] £ 15

2 Who said what? After listening to the story decide whether the following sentences refer to Buster (B), Nicholas (N), Lewis (L), Driscoll (D) or Miss Simpson (S).

	B	N	L	D	S
a. 'Are you deaf or just stupid?'	☐	☐	☐	☐	☐
b. 'I'm really wet.'	☐	☐	☐	☐	☐
c. 'You've done a very good job.'	☐	☐	☐	☐	☐
d. 'Run, rabbit, run.'	☐	☐	☐	☐	☐
e. 'Don't forget the spades.'	☐	☐	☐	☐	☐
f. 'It's a map of Simpson's garden.'	☐	☐	☐	☐	☐
g. 'You're trespassing.'	☐	☐	☐	☐	☐
h. 'Good Lord!'	☐	☐	☐	☐	☐

A Strange Case

Before reading

1 **How superstitious are you? Do you believe in fate?**

	YES	NO
• Have you got a lucky number?	☐	☐
What is it?		
• Do you often read your horoscope in magazines?	☐	☐
How often?		
• Do you think it's unlucky to walk under a ladder?	☐	☐
• If you see a black cat do you think it's lucky?	☐	☐
• Have you ever been to a fortune teller?	☐	☐
What did they say?		
• Do you believe in ghosts?	☐	☐
• Do you think Friday, 17th is unlucky?	☐	☐
• Do you think dreams foretell the future?	☐	☐
• Have you got a lucky object?	☐	☐
What is it?		

2 **Write three things you are frightened of:**

....

....

....

3 **How many words can you find in the box? Give yourself a time limit – 10 minutes. There is also a nine-letter word. Can you guess what it is?**

P	I	L
C	O	M
A	E	N

112

A Strange Case

As a police detective, I've seen and heard many strange and unusual things. I suppose that after forty years of service this is only to be expected. However, I thought nothing could surprise me... That was until I met Mr Perch! 5

Poor old Perch – a tall, elegant man. I'll never forget him. When he came to the police station one morning and told me his incredible story, I confess, I thought he was senile. [1] He told me that he was going to be murdered [2] – later that night. I thought that he had invented the story just to get some attention, and this made me feel sorry for him. There was something about him that reminded me of my Uncle Henry. 10

---

1. **senile** ['siːnaɪl] : not very intelligent because of old age.
2. **murdered** : killed by a person intentionally.

They had the same walk and the same way of speaking. Clear and precise. I couldn't send him away. It was almost lunch time so I asked him to stay for a while and chat. [1]

He was an intelligent man. We talked about all sorts of things. Politics, the Second World War, even the weather. I remember wondering [2] why a man like him had become obsessed with this idea of murder. When he told me that he was a widower, [3] I understood. He also had no children and no relatives. He was completely alone. I offered him a cup of coffee but he refused. He said that he had to go, but first he made me promise not to look for his murderer. He added that his wife had appeared to him in a dream and had told him what was going to happen to him. I asked him if he wanted protection and promised to send him someone later that evening. When he refused, I lost my patience! I had enough cases to solve without worrying about crimes that had not yet been committed. [4] Perch stood up and turned to leave. He said that he did not want protection – he was looking forward to seeing his wife again. He was so convincing that I almost believed him.

Through the glass door I could see Marshall coming towards my office. He was holding the report that I was

---

1. **chat** : talk informally.
2. **wondering** : asking myself.
3. **widower** : a man whose wife has died.
4. **committed** : 'to commit a crime' means to do something illegal.

A StrAnge CaSe

waiting for. I signalled for him to wait outside, then I   35
accompanied Perch to the door. He kept repeating that after
his death he did not want us to look for the murderer. It was a
waste of time, [1] he said. The criminal would get the
punishment that he deserved.

As I opened the door, I asked him why. Why should   40
someone want to murder him? Did he have any enemies?

When he pulled out a thick wad [2] of banknotes
from his pocket, I was shocked. I told him
that he was looking for trouble and
advised him to go to the bank and
deposit the money before he went
home. He just laughed...

The last thing he said before leaving
was, 'man cannot change his destiny.'

I watched him leave, and wondered if I would ever see him   50
again. When Marshall came into my office, I told him about
Perch's visit. Marshall was new and did not have much
experience. I thought he would laugh at Perch's story, but he
didn't. He seemed quite worried. He asked me for the old
man's address, and offered to go and see if he needed   55
anything. I was surprised and pleased at his offer, but I didn't
really think it was necessary for him to go and see Perch.

---

1. **waste of time** : unnecessary time used looking for the murderer.
2. **wad** : large amount of notes pressed together.

Work kept me busy for most of the day, and I forget about
Perch's visit. When I received the phone call in the early
60 hours of the morning, I knew that Perch was involved. A boy
walking his dog had found a body. I rushed [1] to the scene of
the crime and discovered that it was old Perch. He'd been hit
on the back of the head with a heavy object, just a few metres
away from his home. I'll never forget the expression on his
65 face. His lips smiled and he looked happy. I like to think that
he had met his wife after all.

The money that he'd shown me had been stolen – the thief [2]
had also taken his wedding ring. A voice in my head kept
saying, "you see, I told you so!"

70 Even though I had promised Perch not to look for the
murderer, I had to do my job. Besides, I wanted to find the
criminal and make him pay for what he had done.

I spent all morning looking through the computer files for
possible suspects, and I found plenty. [3] It was such an easy job
75 robbing an old man – it could have been anyone!

Marshall wanted to go and pay them a visit that very day,
but I was tired. I had a headache [4] and I couldn't stop thinking
of Perch and the tragic way he had died. I considered myself

1. **rushed** : went quickly.
2. **thief** : person who steals.
3. **plenty** : lots.
4. **headache** : pain in the head.

A Strange Case

responsible. If only I had accompanied him home... If only I
had convinced him to take the money to the bank...   80

If only...

Marshall and I questioned a few of our suspects. They all
seemed to have an alibi so nobody was arrested. Marshall was
especially interested in finding the criminal. The death of the
old man seemed to trouble him in some way.   85

Days passed and we were getting nowhere. I had taken this
particular case to heart [1] and one day I even dreamt of old
Perch. He was sitting on a park bench, next to a pleasant
looking woman. I presumed that this was his wife. He lifted a
hand and pointed at me.   90

'Remember your promise!' he said. 'The thief will be
punished. Have patience.'

As in all dreams, I woke up before I had a chance to answer
him. The next morning I had an appointment with Marshall at
the office. As I sat waiting I heard a voice in my ear.   95

'Detective Galloway, don't forget your promise!'

It was Perch's voice. I turned around expecting to find
someone behind me, but there was nobody there.

I was under pressure and I needed to solve this case in a
hurry!   100

Three days had passed since Perch's death. I had plenty of
work to keep me occupied, but I could not stop thinking about

1. **to heart** : personally.

A StrAnge CaSe

old Perch. It was half past ten when
Marshall arrived bringing me my
mid-morning coffee and sandwiches.
I wasn't hungry so I told him to take a
break [1] himself.

We talked about Perch. There was
something that I hadn't told Marshall.
Perch had showed me a note he had written for me and had
wrapped it around the wad of money. In this, he explained
how the thief would be punished.

I was about to tell him about this when he said something
that puzzled me. He said that he didn't think the thief would
get the punishment that Perch had predicted – it was unlikely
for someone to choke [2] on a piece of bread... Exactly what
Perch had written in his note! How did Marshall know about
this? Unless he was the murderer...

He sat in front of me calmly eating the sandwiches. I stood
up and demanded to know who had given him this
information. When had he seen the note? His face grew white
and he realized that he had made a mistake. He tried to find
an excuse, then he suddenly started to cough. I waited for him
to stop but he didn't. He just carried on coughing and gasping
for breath. [3] I didn't know what to do. I tried hitting him hard

110

115

120

125

1. **break** : rest.
2. **choke** : stop breathing because of something in the throat.
3. **gasping for breath** [breθ] : having difficulty in breathing.

on the back, but it was no use. I rushed to the office door and called for Patterson and Taylor. By the time they reached the office, Marshall lay on the floor. He was already blue in the face. Patterson pulled him to his feet, and I watched helplessly

130 as they tried to force the piece of bread out of his throat. Yes, the piece of bread that Perch had warned me about!

Unfortunately for Marshall, there was nothing that could be done to save him. Patterson lowered him to the ground and we called

135 the coroner. [1] I suddenly felt ill.

After Marshall's death, I made a few enquiries. Marshall had been a gambler. [2] He had lost a lot of money in a poker game, and had got into bad company.

140 He had a long list of debts to pay and some of his creditors were dangerous people. When he had seen the wad of notes that Perch carried about with him, he could not resist the opportunity of getting himself out of trouble. His uniform did not mean much to him – he was only

145 interested in himself. This explained his concern and the reason why he was so interested in the case.

The case had been solved without any help from me or my colleagues! Perch had been right, and now he could rest in peace.

---

1. **coroner** : official who enquires into the cause of death.
2. **gambler** : person who spends money playing games in order to win more money.

After reading

1 **Choose the correct answer.**

a. The detective first met Perch
☐ in the evening.
☐ in the afternoon.
☐ in the morning.

b. Perch stayed in the office and had
☐ a drink.
☐ a chat.
☐ a sandwich.

c. Perch was murdered because he had
☐ lots of enemies.
☐ lots of money.
☐ lots of friends.

d. The body was found
☐ in a field.
☐ near Perch's home.
☐ in Perch's living room.

e. Perch's body was found by
☐ a dog.
☐ a young boy.
☐ the police.

f. The murderer was discovered by
☐ Detective Galloway.
☐ Marshall.
☐ Patterson and Taylor.

g. Marshall stole the money because
☐ he wanted to go on holiday.
☐ he wanted to go and play cards.
☐ he had money problems.

2 **A** **Choose the correct plural form.**

a.	daisys	daisyes	daisies
b.	eyes	eies	eye
c.	mens	mans	men
d.	noises	noisys	noisyes
e.	watchs	watches	waches
f.	wifes	wives	wifs
g.	mouses	mices	mice
h.	forks	forkes	fork
i.	machs	matches	matchs

B **What's the plural of:**

a. child ....

b. foot ....

c. woman ....

d. person ....

e. tooth ....

f. trousers ....

g. jeans ....

h. rat ....

i. penny ....

l. man ....

m. knife ....

n. glasses ....

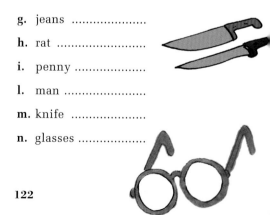

122

3 Put the words in the box into the correct column (refer to the story).

> widower   meet   hard   intelligent   towards   his
> into   chat   body   calmly   old   at   search   bread
> helplessly   our   behind   wonder   in front of

Adjective	Preposition	Verb	Noun	Adverb
....	....	....	....	....
....	....	....	....	....
....	....	....	....	....
....	....	....	....	....
....	....	....	....	....

4 Find the Simple Past of these irregular verbs in the word square. All the verbs are in the story.

> stand   hear   wake   make   tell   send   see   keep
> find   hit   be   have   meet   grow   feel   lose   go

S	A	W	N	A	D	F	G	H	T
M	E	W	H	I	T	O	M	E	T
A	K	E	P	T	M	U	I	A	O
D	S	E	N	T	V	N	L	R	L
E	W	F	E	L	T	D	W	D	D
S	T	O	O	D	Z	E	E	A	P
N	X	Z	L	O	S	T	P	Y	S
P	B	G	R	E	W	W	E	N	T
W	O	K	E	U	H	A	D	Z	Q

5 CROSSWORD

Across

4. Past tense of 'read'
5. Perch was murdered in the early hours of the ....
8. Go .... school; go .... the cinema; go .... the park
10. I, you, she, he, ..., we, you, they
11. Opposite of 'young'
12. A pain in the head
14. The Inspector received this one morning
16. It is sometimes the colour of the sky and the sea
19. Watch a film, see a rainbow but .... at a picture
20. Marshall was one of these
23. Part of the face
24. Perch did not have any friends or relatives. He was lneao.

Down

1. A pet
2. A number before two
3. Abbreviation for morning
6. When they found the body, there was .... in the pockets
7. Past tense of 'take'
8. I don't like coffee, I prefer ....
9. Something you do when you sleep
13. Opposite of 'alive'
14. Perch went to the .... for help
15. It's cold in here – close the rodo
17. Pavarotti is famous for his ....
18. Not very well
21. If you put water into the freezer it turns into this
22. Would you like a cup of tea? ...., thanks.

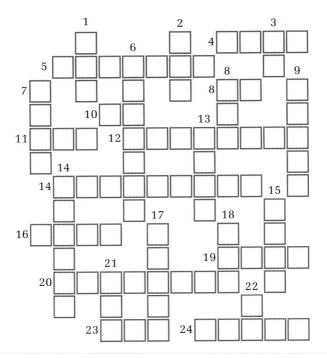

Listening

1 A Listen to the story and decide which sentence is true (T) or false (F).

	T	F
a. Perch reminded the Inspector of his uncle.	☐	☐
b. They talked about Uncle Henry.	☐	☐
c. Perch was not worried about dying.	☐	☐
d. The thief only stole his money.	☐	☐

e. The Inspector worked on the case all morning. ☐ ☐

f. Marshall was a friend of Mr Perch's. ☐ ☐

g. The Inspector knew how the murderer
   was going to die. ☐ ☐

h. Marshall choked on a piece of cake. ☐ ☐

B Now complete the summary.

One day a man called Mr .... came to see me in the police

station. He had a very strange .... to tell. He said he was going

to be murdered very near in the future but he did not want me to look

for his .... I told Marshall, another police officer, about the

visit and then carried on working. The next .... I heard that

Perch was dead and that his money and wedding .... had been

stolen. I started to look for the murderer with .... help.

.... days later I was with Marshall in my office – it was

lunchtime and we were having a cup of .... and eating some

.... We were discussing Perch's case when Marshall said

something that made me very suspicious. Suddenly he

started............... on his sandwich. He died exactly how Perch had

predicted – choking on a piece of ....

TEST YOUR MEMORY

Now that you have read all the stories in the book do this quiz. How much can you remember?

1. What was Trudy's problem?

   ....

2. Why did the butler leave Cranberry?

   ....

3. What were the crosses on Simpson's map?

   ....

4. Who got promotion?

   ....

5. What was in the fridge?

   ....

6. How did Ian get to Littlepoint?

   ....

7. Why was Madame Eve's living room empty?

   ....

8. How did Olive die?

   ....

9. Who found Mr Perch's body?

   ....

10. Name the characters in "Simpson's Buried Treasure".

    ....

11. Name three things Marge liked eating.

    ....

12. How did Perch know he was going to die?

    ....

13. What was the 'little black object'?

    ....

14. Nicholas's nickname.

    ....

15. Who was Trudy's boyfriend?

    ....

16. When was Perch's body discovered?

    ....

17. How old were Marge and Olive?

    ....

18. What did Cranberry bury?

    ....

19. How did Marshall die?

    ....

20. How many letters did Trudy write to Susan?

    ....

21. How did Ian get to Cliffview?

    ....

22. What colour hair did Miss Simpson have?

    ....

23. Where did Madame Eve live?

    ....

24. Who was Alfred?

    ....

Which story did you like best? Why?

....